Bo plays golf

RJG
Publishing

First published in the UK in 2021
by RJG Publishing

ISBN 978-1-9196012-8-1

First edition

A CIP record for this book is available from the British Library.

Typeset by Marten Sealby
Illustrations by Anica

All the proceeds from the sale of this book will be going to
Evelina Children's Hospital.

To my amazing wife, Laura, thank you for all you do for us.
To our boys, AJ and Rory, thank you for choosing us to make
our family complete – you are both awesome.

To the NHS, thank you for all you have done through the pandemic
but, even before this, you have had an integral part to play in ensuring
both of our boys are still with us today. You are the unsung heroes
of our country and we will be forever grateful.

Can you find the trophy
on every page?

This sporting adventure book belongs to:

_____

Bo was rummaging through his cupboard one day.

This was great fun, but wait, what's hiding back there?

Could it be toys or some hidden treasure?

Can you guess why he is one excited little bear?

A bag clinked and clanked as it spilled out the cupboard.

Then there they were, the clubs he had always wanted.

Along with some balls and a glove for good measure.

Oh yes, he thought, all my wishes have been granted.

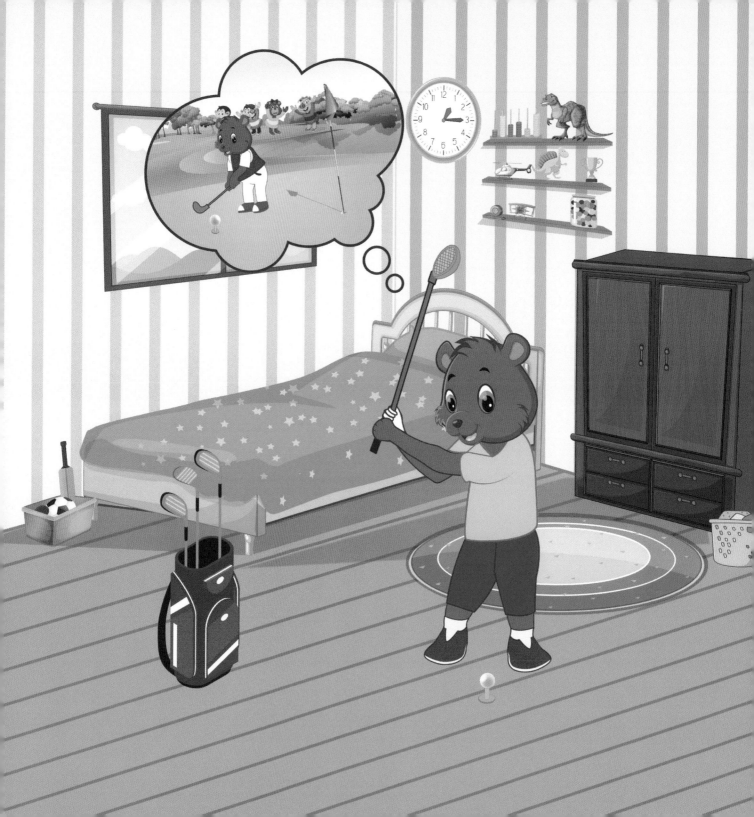

The time has come to try out his swing,

A new skill to perfect, Bo gives it a go

I can do this, he says to himself

And with a wry smile, ponders, could I turn pro?

Bo knew that if he didn't try hard, he stood no chance
So he hopped on his bike and off to the range he went.
Got himself a bucket of balls and lined up his stance
Oh no, a duffed shot and now his 8 iron is bent!

Not one to worry about this sort of thing,

Bo knows he needs to keep doing his best.

So with his next club, off the ball flies.

A beginner? No one would ever have guessed.

Time for the course with his friend.

George the goat enjoys playing too.

Bags on their backs, a glove on one hand,

Bo teed up and off the ball flew.

There it lay in the dreaded bunker,

Nestled in the sand, up against the lip.

He shuffled his feet and closed his eyes,

A hopeful swing and what a lucky chip!

A downhill putt that looks a bit tricky,

Bo thinks it's best to hit it slightly left to right.

Around the pitch mark towards the pin,

It gently rolls, plops in the cup and out of sight!

They get to a par 5 that seems a real test.

Bo pulls out his driver and grips it quite tight,

Over the bunker and through the bushes.

Whoops! He forgot to shout "Fore right!"

The course is in great shape with a par 3 next,

Water to the right with some ducks having fun.

Bo puts his head down and strikes it close.

My oh my, that was almost a hole in one.

Down the 18th the two friends walk.

The game is so close, who will win?

Bo takes aim, a little wiggle and off it goes

"Yes!" he shouts, "It's next to the pin!"

With a handshake and a smile,

The two friends ponder about maybe having another round.

But at the same time Bo let's his mind wander...

Could he lift the Woggle Cup on St. Andrews hallowed ground?

Birdie: This is when a golfer gets it in the hole in one less shot than normal.

Fore: A person should shout "fore" if they hit a wayward shot to warn other people that a ball may be coming their way.

Lip: This is the edge of a bunker where the sand meets the grass.

Pitch mark: When a ball lands on the green, it can sometimes leave a mark (it is good manners to repair these for other golfers).

Range: This is a practice area for golfers where they can hit lots of balls.

Woggle Cup: The ultimate trophy in the world of imaginary golf – did you spot one on each page?

Printed in Great Britain
by Amazon